This Book Belongs To:

_____

COPYRIGHT © 2003 Nanci Bell
Gander Publishing
P.O. Box 780
Avila Beach, CA 93424
805-541-5523 • 800-554-1819

SEEING STARS AND CATCH A STAR ARE REGISTERED TRADEMARKS OF NANCI BELL.

20   19   18   17   5   6   7   8

978-0-945856-26-9

5-171201

Overview and Directions

The *Catch a Star*® workbooks develop oral vocabulary, reading, and spelling for the most commonly used words in English, the Star Words in the *Seeing Stars*® program.

Each workbook, or Warp, moves students sequentially through fifty Star Words. The students develop symbol imagery, phonological processing, and concept imagery skills as well as vocabulary, reading, and spelling, as in the *Seeing Stars* and *Visualizing and Verbalizing*® programs.

Ivan the Cat—King of the Neighborhood—narrates each workbook to add humor and interest. The lessons are beneficial for young students or students with language processing challenges, including those with English as a second language.

300 Star Words in the *Catch a Star* Workbook Set:

The six *Catch a Star* workbooks consist of fifty Star Words each. As students progress through the workbooks, the words and sentences become more complex. Decoding skills are reinforced through the repetition of the Star Words in subsequent lessons. Words with multiple definitions often comprise more than one lesson.

Warp 1: Star Words 1-50	**Warp 3: Star Words 101-150**	**Warp 5: Star Words 201-250**
Warp 2: Star Words 51-100	**Warp 4: Star Words 151-200**	**Warp 6: Star Words 251-300**

The Star Words:

The Star Word is placed in the top left corner and in the bottom outside corner of each page for easy reference. The definition of the word is in small print for the instructor.

The Sentences:

Simple sentences use the Star Word in context to reinforce word meaning and imagery for the concept and the letters of the word. This helps students place both the orthography and meaning of the word in memory.

1 The air is cold, so Ivan will stay in bed.

Your Language Stimulates Imagery:

Your language needs to direct students to their own imagery. *"What do you **picture** for the word skyscraper?"*

There are two types of imagery to be developed:

1) *Concept imagery for vocabulary and comprehension*
   To develop concept imagery for oral vocabulary, ask, *"What do you picture for the meaning of the word skyscraper?"*
   To develop concept imagery for comprehension from the sentence, ask, *"What did those words make you picture?"*
2) *Symbol imagery for decoding and spelling*
   To develop symbol imagery for phonological and orthographic processing, ask, *"What letters did you picture for the word? What is the second letter you pictured? What is the last letter you pictured?"* Vary your questions for each word.

Trace/Finger-Write/Write the Word:

These sections develop symbol imagery to help students visually imprint the word in their own imagery/memory.

Have your students:
1) slowly trace each word with their finger while saying each letter aloud,
2) finger-write the word in the space provided, again saying each letter name aloud, and
3) write the word in the last space and again saying each letter aloud.

Be sure to question phonological irregularities to ensure a word is not only processed phonetically but also imaged orthographically and held in visual memory. For example, in the word **have**, ask students to note what part of the word doesn't play fair and then specifically visualize that letter. *"What is the last letter you pictured in the word have?"*

Use the Star Word in a Sentence:

Have your students create their own sentence using the Star Word. This uses the word in context and develops the student's imagery to be stored and retrieved later. The student can either dictate or write the sentence.

Hey everyone, it's your learning partner, Ivan—King of the Neighborhood. In fact, I have expanded my neighborhood to include the Moon, the planets, and the stars—in other words—OUTER SPACE!

This book is called Warp 4, and it takes us to our fourth space destination—Mars. Mars is sometimes referred to as the Red Planet. Can you guess what color it is? It's very windy there. Mars has dust storms that can last several months. Hmmm...mice like dusty places...Mars needs mice!

This *Catch a Star* workbook will help you develop your vocabulary using the words that pop up most often in English. In cat language, those words would include *very*, as in "Ivan is *very* hungry. Let's feed him!" and *picture*, as in "Ivan can *picture* you getting him a big fish pie."

Each book, or Warp, of the series will blast you from Star Word to Star Word on an intergalactic learning adventure. The aliens (yes, I said aliens) and I will be on hand to help by pointing things out, and you will also find me posing for many of the pictures.

Everyone knows that learning can be fun, whether you're in a classroom or in outer space about a million miles from the nearest litter box. And I know you can do this and have fun, too. Hey, if I can find mice in a dust storm, you can finish this book!

air

the air we breathe; the gases that surround the Earth; the sky

 1 The air is cold, so Ivan will stay in bed.

 2 Bill's red kite flew up into the air.

 3 The tire had no air in it.

 4 Ivan saw the birds fly in the air.

Tom let all the air out of the balloon.

Trace the word:

air

Finger-write the word:

Write the word:

Use the word in your own sentence: _____

_____

_____

air

still

silent or calm; not moving

 1 Ben dove into the clear still water.

 2 Mike's mom told him to sit still.

 3 The kids stood as still as statues.

 4 Ivan stays still while he watches the fish tank.

Ivan sat still until the mouse came back.

Trace the word:

still

Finger-write the word:

Write the word:

Use the word in your own sentence: _____

_____

_____

still

2

still

even or yet; until a certain time

 1. Ivan ate six hot dogs, and he still wants pie.

 2. Jill has ten dolls, but she still wants more.

 3. Bob still will not clean his room.

 4. At ten o'clock, Ivan was still eating.

Ivan was still in bed when the kids got home.

Trace the word:

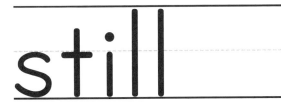

Finger-write the word:

_____

_____

Write the word:

_____

_____

Use the word in your own sentence: _____

_____

_____

still

across; on top of

 Jim will jump over the log.

 Ivan jumped over the dog.

 The kids ran over the sand.

 Ivan put his paw over the fish.

Pat had to step over Ivan.

Trace the word:

Finger-write the word:

Write the word:

over

Use the word in your own sentence: _____

over

down; to the other side

 Jill bent over to pick up the coin on the floor.

 Dan stood on the chair and was careful not to fall over.

 Ivan can roll over onto his back.

 Did Ivan push the fish tank over?

Did Rod trip and fall over?

Trace the word:

over

Finger-write the word:

Write the word:

Use the word in your own sentence: _____

_____

_____

over

alone of its kind

 There are only three fish in Ivan's fish tank.

 Now there are only two fish in Ivan's fish tank.

 Tom has three dogs, but only one fat cat.

 Ivan is the only cat that talks.

Ivan was the only one to get an A on the test.

Trace the word:

only

Finger-write the word:

Write the word:

Use the word in your own sentence: _____

_____

_____

only

6

little

small in size or amount; not much

 1 Ivan put a little jam on his tuna.

 2 Sue had a little bite of cake.

 3 Ivan likes to play with the little fish.

 4 A little fish swam in Ivan's water dish, but not for long!

Matt put a little milk in his tea.

Trace the word:

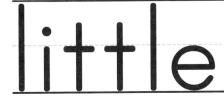

little

Finger-write the word:

Write the word:

Use the word in your own sentence: _____

_____

_____

little

young

 Tom gave a doll to his little sister.

 The little kids like to play on the slide.

 The little boy ran to his mom.

 The little kittens played with Ivan's tail.

Ivan was so cute when he was little.

Trace the word:

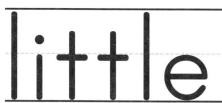

Finger-write the word:

Write the word:

Use the word in your own sentence: _____

_____

_____

little

 1 Tom did not know that Ivan ate his lunch.

 2 Do you know why a cat is in the refrigerator?

 3 Does Ivan know there is a bug in his dish?

 4 Does Matt know where Ivan hid the tuna?

Ed does not know where his pig went.

Trace the word:

know

Finger-write the word:

Write the word:

Use the word in your own sentence: _____

to have information or to be acquainted with; to be sure of something

know

place

a specific area, building, home, or business

1 Ivan put the fish back in his place.

2 The cats all went to Ivan's place for lunch.

3 Ivan lives in a nice place by the park.

4 Tom will set Ivan's dish in its place.

Ivan will put the fish back in its place.

Trace the word:

place

Finger-write the word:

Write the word:

Use the word in your own sentence: _____

_____

place

to put somewhere

 1 Did Jan place her coat on the hook?

 2 Did Tom place the pie in Ivan's food dish?

 3 Jill had to place the food far from Ivan.

 4 Did Ivan place his dish near the fish tank?

Jim will place the vase on the desk.

Trace the word:

place

Finger-write the word:

_____

Write the word:

_____

Use the word in your own sentence: _____

_____

_____

place

very

extremely

 1 Ivan can eat very well.

 2 Ivan is always very hungry.

 3 Ivan ate a very big fish for lunch, and then another.

 4 Ivan was very sleepy, so he took a nap.

Mike is very tall.

Trace the word:

very

Finger-write the word:

Write the word:

Use the word in your own sentence: _____

_____

very

 1. Dan went to bed after he took a bath.

 2. Tom came home after Jill had left.

 3. After dinner, Ivan went to the refrigerator for a snack.

 4. After Ivan had a snack, he went to the fish tank.

later; behind

After lunch, Ivan took a nap.

Trace the word:

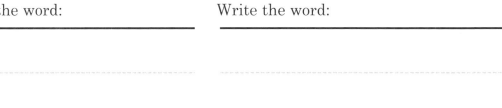

after

Finger-write the word:

_____

Write the word:

_____

Use the word in your own sentence: _____

_____

_____

after

think

to have an opinion; to believe

 1. Ann thinks that Bob is very cute.

 2. Tom and Bill think Ivan ate the pie.

 3. Ivan thinks the dog ate his red eggs and fish.

 4. Does Ivan think he can live in the refrigerator?

Tim thinks it will rain.

Trace the word:

think

Finger-write the word:

Write the word:

Use the word in your own sentence: _____

_____

think

wonderful (informal)

 1 Bob had a great time at the party.

 2 Ivan is great at playing hide and seek.

 3 The cake Tom made was great.

 4 Ivan is a great, smart, fat cat.

Ivan is a great singer.

Trace the word:

great

Finger-write the word:

Write the word:

Use the word in your own sentence: _____

great

 1 Juan is at the park. Tom is also there.

 2 Tom has a cat and he also has a dog.

 3 Ivan ate ham. He also ate jam. He also ate cake.

 4 Ivan ate fish. He also ate a hot dog. He also ate red eggs.

Ivan likes cake. He also likes pie.

in addition; too

Trace the word:

also

Finger-write the word:

Write the word:

Use the word in your own sentence: _____

_____

also

large

big in size or amount

 1 Ivan is a large fat cat.

 2 Ivan ran away from the large dog.

 3 Kim drank a large glass of milk.

 4 Ivan ate a large fish from the lake.

Bob has very large feet.

Trace the word: _____

large

Finger-write the word: _____

Write the word: _____

Use the word in your own sentence: _____

_____

_____

large

read

to understand the meaning of written language

 1 Ivan can read!

 2 Tom sometimes reads to Ivan.

 3 Ivan likes to read books about food.

 4 Can you believe a cat can read?

Ivan can read "Catch a Star." Can you?

Trace the word:

read

Finger-write the word:

_____

_____

Write the word:

_____

_____

Use the word in your own sentence: _____

_____

_____

read

18

land

earth; the ground; property

 1 The kids play baseball on the land next to the school.

 2 The land on Mars is red.

 3 The land was wet and muddy from the rain.

 4 Ivan will help Ken plant corn on his land.

Ivan looked at the land around him.

Trace the word:

land

Finger-write the word:

Write the word:

Use the word in your own sentence: _____

land

to arrive somewhere, especially by air

 1 The plane had to land on a small road.

 2 Tim's plane will land soon.

 3 Bob likes to jump off the bed and land on his feet.

 4 Did a fly land on Ivan's cake?

Jan saw Ivan trip and land in the cake.

Trace the word:

land

Finger-write the word:

Write the word:

Use the word in your own sentence: _____

_____

land

move

to change one's home or position

 1 Did Ivan move the fish?

 2 Tom will move the fish to the fish tank.

 3 Did Ivan move the pie from the table?

 4 Ivan will not move from Tom's bed.

Kim had to move the ham away from Ivan.

Trace the word: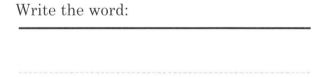

Finger-write the word: _____

Write the word: _____

move _____ _____

Use the word in your own sentence: _____

_____

_____

move

kind

nice, gentle

 1 Ivan sat next to a kind old man.

 2 The kind man gave Ivan his food.

 3 The teacher gave Tom a kind smile.

 4 Ivan is not very kind to fish.

Tim was kind and let Ivan have his pie.

Trace the word:

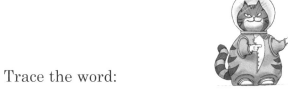

kind

Finger-write the word:

_____

_____

Write the word:

_____

_____

Use the word in your own sentence: _____

_____

kind

kind

a sort; a category, group, or class

 1 What kind of cake does Ivan like?

 2 Ivan likes all kinds of food.

 3 What kind of dog does Mike have?

 4 What kind of jam did Ivan put on his fish pie?

Ivan has three kinds of fish.

Trace the word:

Finger-write the word:

Write the word:

kind

_____

_____

_____

_____

Use the word in your own sentence: _____

_____

_____

kind

once more

 1   Ivan ate his breakfast then ate again.

 2   Ivan ate his lunch then ate again.

 3   The boys want to go down the slide again.

 4   Ivan woke up and went back to sleep again.

Ivan sang the same song again and again.

Trace the word:

Finger-write the word:

Write the word:

again

Use the word in your own sentence: _____

_____

_____

again

to name or write the letters of a word

 Ivan can spell.

 Tom likes to spell words out loud in class.

 Ann could spell all of the words on the list.

 Can you spell Ivan?

Ivan can spell the word tuna.

Trace the word:

spell

Finger-write the word:

Write the word:

Use the word in your own sentence: _____

_____

_____

spell

 1   Ivan ate breakfast at Bob's house.

 2   Ivan ate lunch at Tom's house.

 3   Ivan ate dinner at Kim's house.

 4   Ivan ate everything in Gunny's house.

Ivan ate a snack at Bill's house.

Trace the word:

house

Finger-write the word:

Write the word:

Use the word in your own sentence: _____

_____

house

the sharp end of an object

 1 The point of the pencil broke.

 2 Ann made a star with five points.

 3 Tim pushed the point of the tack into the wall.

 4 The point of Ivan's claw is very sharp.

The point of the arrow hit the target.

Trace the word:

point

Finger-write the word:

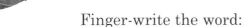

Write the word:

Use the word in your own sentence: _____

_____

point

point

a unit for scoring or counting

 Tom made ten points in the game.

 Dan's team won the game by two points.

 Dee only missed one point on the test.

 In the cat show, Ivan got five points for his great smile.

Jill kicked the ball and made a point.

Trace the word:

point

Finger-write the word:

_____

Write the word:

_____

Use the word in your own sentence: _____

_____

_____

point

point

to draw attention to someone or something by using one's finger

 It is not nice to point.

 Ivan will point to the fish he wants.

 Did Ivan point to the little dog?

 Did Ivan point to his empty food dish?

Ivan always points at his dish when he is hungry.

Trace the word:

point

Finger-write the word:

Write the word:

Use the word in your own sentence: _____

_____

_____

point

one piece of paper in a book, newspaper, or magazine

 How many pages did Tom read?

 Bob will turn the pages as Ivan reads.

 Mike drew a star on each page.

 Ivan sat on the front page of the newspaper.

Did Ivan bite one page of the book?

Trace the word:

Finger-write the word:

Write the word:

page

Use the word in your own sentence: _____

_____

_____

page

a female parent

 1 Ivan's mother went with him to the zoo.

 2 Ivan and his mother went to the park.

 3 Ivan is fat like his mother.

 4 Ivan looks like his mother.

Ivan will give his mother a big hug.

Trace the word:

mother

Finger-write the word: _____

Write the word: _____

_____

Use the word in your own sentence: _____

_____

_____

mother

father

a male parent

 Tom is short like his father.

 Ivan's father went with him to the park.

 Ivan gave some tuna to his father.

 Ivan went to the fish tank with his father.

Ivan will give his father a big hug.

Trace the word:

father

Finger-write the word:

Write the word:

Use the word in your own sentence: _____

father

a noise; something that is heard

 The puppy made a cute little sound.

 Tom blew, but no sound came out of the horn.

 What sound does a hen make?

 Ivan made a sound when he dropped his sandwich.

The loud sound made
Ivan jump.

Trace the word:

Finger-write the word:

_____

_____

Write the word:

_____

_____

Use the word in your own sentence: _____

_____

_____

33

sound

 1 Kim has a new teacher this year.

 2 Ivan ate one hundred fish pies last year.

 3 Tom gets new boots each year.

 4 Ivan will get a new fish tank next year.

year

a period of twelve months; 365 days

Ivan is three years old.

Trace the word:

year

Finger-write the word:

_____

Write the word:

_____

Use the word in your own sentence: _____

_____

_____

year

thing

an object

 1 All of Jill's things fell out of her bag.

 2 Ivan got many things for his birthday.

 3 Tom set all of his things on the desk.

 4 What is that thing in Ivan's water dish?

Ann put a lot of bows and things in Ivan's fur.

Trace the word:

Finger-write the word:

Write the word:

Use the word in your own sentence: _____

_____

_____

thing

sentence

a group of words put together to make a statement

 1 Dee will read the sentence to her class.

 2 Dan wrote a very long sentence.

 3 Joe had to write a sentence for each spelling word.

 4 Ivan cannot write a sentence.

Ivan ate all of the food

Tom wrote a sentence about Ivan.

Trace the word:

Finger-write the word:

Write the word:

sentence

_____

_____

Use the word in your own sentence: _____

_____

sentence

in and out; in the middle of

 Bill rode his bike through town.

 Ivan ran through the house looking for the mouse.

 Did Tom look through the book?

 Ivan went through the park on his way home.

A bird flew through the air over Ivan.

Trace the word:

through

Finger-write the word:

Write the word:

Use the word in your own sentence: _____

through

earlier in time

 Before Ivan eats, he will take a nap.

 Ivan ate a hot dog before he had lunch.

 Tom will feed Ivan again before he goes to bed.

 Before Ivan goes to bed, he will eat a snack.

Ivan took a bath before he went to bed.

Trace the word:

before

Finger-write the word:

Write the word:

Use the word in your own sentence: _____

_____

before

not nice; cruel

 1 The little kitten was mean to his brother.

 2 It was mean of Tom not to give any cake to Ivan.

 3 The mean kid took Jill's doll.

 4 Pat was mean and did not give Ivan any pie.

Ivan did not like the mean dog next door.

Trace the word:

mean

Finger-write the word:

Write the word:

Use the word in your own sentence: _____

_____

_____

mean

mean

to represent; to intend

 1 What does a red light mean?

 2 A green light means go.

 3 Ivan did not mean to wake up Tom.

 4 Did Ivan mean to eat the fish?

Bob did not mean to eat Ivan's lunch.

Trace the word: _____

mean

Finger-write the word: _____

_____

Write the word: _____

_____

Use the word in your own sentence: _____

_____

_____

mean

following

the next one in time or order; to go after someone or something

 1 Following breakfast, Ivan will take a nap.

 2 Ivan will eat lunch following his nap.

 3 Following lunch, Ivan will eat a snack.

 4 Ivan was following the mouse around the house.

Ivan was following the mouse to the cheese.

Trace the word:

Finger-write the word:

Write the word:

following

_____

_____

Use the word in your own sentence: _____

_____

following

around

surrounding; in a circle

 1 The kittens like to chase Ivan around the house.

 2 Bob ran around the block.

 3 Kim spun around until she fell down.

 4 The fish swam around in Ivan's dish.

Ivan chased his tail around and around.

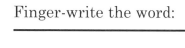

Trace the word:

around

Finger-write the word:

Write the word:

Use the word in your own sentence: _____

_____

around

 1 Bill woke up around nine o'clock.

 2 Around ten kids went to the game.

 3 Ivan eats around ten fish pies a week.

 4 Ivan eats around six meals a day.

around

approximately, about

Ivan is around the same size as the pig.

Trace the word:

around

Finger-write the word:

Write the word:

Use the word in your own sentence: _____

around

form

to shape or make something

1 Tom will form the clay into a vase.

2 Did a crowd form around Ivan at the cat show?

3 Jan will form popcorn balls for the party.

4 Did Ivan form his cat food into the shape of a fish?

The kids had to form a line before class.

Trace the word:

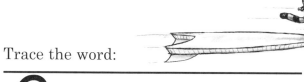

form

Finger-write the word:

Write the word:

Use the word in your own sentence: _____

_____

_____

form

one more; a different one

 Ann put one fish in Ivan's fish tank. Then she put in another.

 Ivan chased one dog and then another.

 Ivan ate five hot dogs. Then he ate another.

 Ivan was still hungry after he ate one fish, so he ate another.

Bob's coat was too small, so Ivan gave him another.

Trace the word:

another

Finger-write the word:

Write the word:

Use the word in your own sentence: _____

_____

_____

another

even

not an odd number; equal

 Ivan ate an even number of fish.

 The race was even almost to the end.

 The score was even after Kim kicked the ball into the net.

 Ann cut two even slices of ham, and Ivan ate them.

Mike cut the cake into nice even slices.

Trace the word:

even

Finger-write the word:

Write the word:

Use the word in your own sentence: _____

_____

_____

even

no matter what; more

 1. Ivan will go to the zoo even if it rains.

 2. Ivan will eat even if he is not hungry.

 3. The cake was even better than the pie.

 4. Ivan can run even faster than the big dog.

Ivan's food dish is even bigger than the dog's.

Trace the word: _____

Finger-write the word: _____

Write the word: _____

even

Use the word in your own sentence: _____

_____

_____

even

 1. Tom ran because he saw the ice cream truck.

 2. Ivan ate all of the cake because he was hungry.

 3. Jim took off his coat because he was hot.

 4. Ivan was sad because his dish was empty.

Ivan was full because he ate all the tuna.

Trace the word:

because

Finger-write the word:

Write the word:

Use the word in your own sentence: _____

_____

because

turn

to move a switch (on or off)

 1 Ivan did not turn on the radio.

 2 The kids did not turn the light off.

 3 Did Matt turn off the stove?

 4 Ivan can turn on the lights.

Ivan is cold, so Jan will turn up the heat.

Trace the word:

turn

Finger-write the word:

Write the word:

Use the word in your own sentence: _____

_____

_____

turn

to become; to change direction

 1 The wind began to turn cold.

 2 The small kitten turned into a big cat.

 3 The dog will turn and run when it sees Ivan.

 4 Did Ivan turn around and see the big dog?

This frog will not turn into a prince.

Trace the word: _____

turn

Finger-write the word: _____

Write the word: _____

Use the word in your own sentence: _____

_____

turn

to invite; to make a request

 1 Tom will ask Sue to the party.

 2 Did Ivan ask for more fish?

 3 Did Ivan ask if he could have some cake?

 4 Did Ivan ask if he could eat everything in the refrigerator?

Al should ask Ivan to give his shoes back.

Trace the word:

ask

Finger-write the word:

Write the word:

 Use the word in your own sentence: _____

_____

_____

ask

not the same

 1 Tom wants a different book.

 2 Ivan ate two different kinds of cake.

 3 Ivan had a different snack every hour.

 4 Ivan eats a different kind of pie each day.

Sue had on two different socks.

Trace the word:

different

Finger-write the word:

_____

_____

Write the word:

_____

_____

Use the word in your own sentence: _____

_____

different

a likeness or image of someone or
something; a photograph

 1 Tom drew a big picture on the wall.

 2 Ann will paint a picture of Ivan.

 3 Tim has a picture of a frog and a duck.

 4 Ivan had a picture of his fish.

Ann drew a picture of Ivan.

Trace the word:

picture

Finger-write the word:

Write the word:

Use the word in your own sentence: _____

_____

_____

picture

to imagine; to form a mental image

 1 The story made Ivan picture a big plate of fish.

 2 Did Tom picture a cow next to a red barn?

 3 What do you picture for a cowboy?

 4 Ivan could picture a big fish pie.

Bob can picture Ivan in his mind.

Trace the word:

picture

Finger-write the word:

Write the word:

Use the word in your own sentence: _____

picture

change

to exchange or switch; to make different

 1 Tom will change his clothes.

 2 Did Ivan change his cake for a bigger one?

 3 Did Ann change her mind and go to the game?

 4 Ivan had to change seats so he could see.

Bill must change his shirt.

Trace the word:

change

Finger-write the word:

Write the word:

Use the word in your own sentence: _____

_____

_____

change

coins or money

 Kim had enough change to get a hot dog.

 Ivan found some change on the floor.

 Ivan gave the change to Tom.

 Tom used his change to buy Ivan a new food dish.

Tom puts his change in his bank.

Trace the word:

Finger-write the word:

Write the word:

change

Use the word in your own sentence: _____

_____

_____

change

animal

any living thing other than plants

 1 Tom has three animals in his house.

 2 Does Ivan have a toy animal?

 3 Ivan ate lunch with the animals.

 4 Ivan does not think he is an animal.

Bob likes to feed the animals on the farm.

Trace the word:

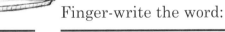

Finger-write the word:

Write the word:

animal

Use the word in your own sentence: _____

_____

_____

animal

letter

any character in an alphabet

 1 Ann drew a big letter A on her paper.

 2 How many letters are in Tom's name?

 3 Matt will try to learn all the letters.

 4 Ivan only knows the letters t-u-n-a.

Kim can write the letters
a, b, and c.

Trace the word:

letter

Finger-write the word:

_____

_____

Write the word:

_____

_____

Use the word in your own sentence: _____

_____

_____

letter

letter

a written or printed message

 1 Tom sends a letter to his friend each week.

 2 Ann keeps her letters in a box.

 3 Tom wrote a long letter to Ivan.

 4 Ivan put a paw print at the end of Ann's letter.

Did Ivan get a letter in the mail?

Trace the word:

letter

Finger-write the word:

_____

_____

_____

Write the word:

_____

_____

_____

Use the word in your own sentence: _____

_____

_____

letter

the solution

 Dee got all of the answers on her test right.

 The answers are in the back of the book.

 Did Tom get the answers right?

 Did Ivan tell Tom the answers?

Who is the best cat?
The answer is Ivan.

Trace the word:

Finger-write the word:

Write the word:

answer

Use the word in your own sentence: _____

_____

_____

answer

60

to respond or reply

 1 Ann answers her mail each day.

 2 Tom wrote to Ivan, but he did not answer.

 3 Joe called Ivan, but he did not answer.

 4 Does Ivan answer when he is called?

Ivan did not answer the door.

Trace the word: _____

Finger-write the word: _____

Write the word: _____

answer _____ _____

Use the word in your own sentence: _____

_____

_____

answer

found

to have located or discovered something

 1 Tom's sock was never found.

 2 Bob found a dollar on the floor.

 3 Ivan found a pie on the table.

 4 Ivan ate the pie he found on the table.

Ivan found a fish in his water dish.

Trace the word:

found

Finger-write the word:

Write the word:

Use the word in your own sentence: _____

_____

_____

found

to try to learn; to investigate carefully

 1 Tom will study hard for the test.

 2 Ivan will not study.

 3 Kim likes to study in her room.

 4 Ivan will study his empty food dish until Tom fills it.

Ivan sat on Tom's books when he tried to study.

Trace the word:

study

Finger-write the word:

Write the word:

Use the word in your own sentence: _____

_____

_____

study

learn

to come to know through study or experience

 1 Dan will learn how to spell.

 2 Did Ivan learn to read?

 3 Tom wants to learn to ride a horse.

 4 Did Ivan learn to open a can of tuna?

Tom and Ivan want to learn to cook.

Trace the word:

learn

 Finger-write the word:

Write the word:

Use the word in your own sentence:

learn

American

of or from the United States

 1 The American flag is red, white, and blue.

 2 Kim's mom is American.

 3 Ivan likes American food.

 4 Ivan likes American food and any other kind of food.

Ivan is an American cat.

Trace the word:

American

Finger-write the word:

_____

Write the word:

_____

Use the word in your own sentence: _____

_____

_____

American

the Earth

 1 Tom wants to fly all over the world.

 2 Ivan is the best cat in the world.

 3 Bob will sail around the world in his boat.

 4 Ivan wants to eat every kind of food in the world.

Tom has a map of the world in his room.

Trace the word:

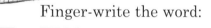

world

Finger-write the word:

Write the word:

Use the word in your own sentence: _____

_____

world